MW00638003

The Man with Bees in His Beard

The Man with
Bees in His Beard

Written and Illustrated by
Brian Dempsey

Chatwin Books
Seattle
2018

Paperback
ISBN 978-1-63398-058-7

Hardcover deluxe
ISBN 978-1-63398-056-3

Copyright © Brian Dempsey 2018. All rights reserved. Written permission must be obtained from the publisher prior to scanning, copying, reproducing or distributing any part of this work.

Published by Chatwin Books, Seattle, Washington.

Orders and inquiries:
Chatwin Books
info@chatwinbooks.com
www.chatwinbooks.com

For Luc

The man with bees in his beard
did not wish for a large house
or the weight of money in his pocket
or even the company of others.

He lived for the soft wind
a path beneath his feet
and the hum of nothing
when everything is quiet.

No one knows how the bees got there
just that they never stung.
He was their home.

I met him once in a wood
around our fire he sang a song.
Not the kind with a beat to make you tap your toes
no, not one with a story that comes in rhyme.

The song was sound
sound that moved
like leaves in a breeze
like water turning slow around stones.

With eyes closed, his body rocked
and the bees sang too.
He and the bees, one and the same.

In the morning he was gone
just some honey for my tea and a note –

Curve of the earth
The moon's rainbow ring
Gone south for flowers
Be back in the spring

The man with bees in his beard
did not wish for bright lights in the city
or things fast and loud
or even fancy clothes.

He lived for the shimmer of stars
for that place where a forest meets a field
and the hum of nothing
when everything is quiet.

No one knows how the bees got there
just that they never stung.
He was their home.

The bees talked to him
and he talked to them.
Not like people telling tall tales
no, not with words you can speak.

The talk was sound
sound deep down
like the way a mountain talks to fog
like roots talk to rain.

Like the hum of nothing
when everything is quiet.

Brian Dempsey has spent much of his grownup life on the West Coast. His art reflects the rocky beaches and mighty evergreens of his home on Vashon Island, Washington and his writing is inspired by myth and Eastern philosophy. You may often find him in his studio drawing, painting, playing guitar or enjoying the hum of nothing.